The Rocket Ship

Story by Julie Bryant
Illustrations by Naomi C Lewis

2

Emma and Matthew loved staying
with their Gran and Grandad.
They had an old house
with lots of rooms to play in.

But best of all, Gran and Grandad
had a big tree in their garden.

One morning,
Matthew looked out the window.
"It's windy again," he said to Emma,
"and we can't go out
and climb the tree."

"It's raining, too," said Emma.
"We will have to play inside today."

That night, the wind blew very hard.

Emma called out to Matthew.
"Matthew," she said. "I'm scared!"

Gran and Grandad
came in to see them.

"It's a very windy night,"
said Grandad.
"Try to go to sleep."

Then...

Crash!

They all ran to look out the window.

"The big tree has fallen over!"
said Gran.

"Oh, no!" said Matthew.
"Now we won't have a tree to climb."

"We are lucky
that it didn't hit the house,"
said Grandad.

Gran gave them a hug.
"Go to sleep," she said.
"The wind will stop blowing soon.
We will have a good look
at the tree in the morning."

The next morning,
they all went out to look
at the tree.

"Oh, dear," said Grandad.

"It was the best tree ever,"
said Emma.
"We could climb into the branches
and hide there.
No one could see us."

"And now I will have to cut it up for firewood," said Grandad.

"Please don't cut it up, Grandad," cried Matthew.
"We could still play on it."

"Yes," said Emma.
"It could be our rocket ship."

"We could fly all over the place in it,"
said Matthew.
"Come on, Emma."

Matthew and Emma
raced over to the tree
and climbed up.

"I'm the captain," said Emma.
"Are you ready for take-off, Matthew?"

"Ready, Captain!" shouted Matthew.
"Ready to fire the rockets... **now**!

10-9-8-7-6-5-4-3-2-1!"

"We have lift-off!"
Emma shouted back at him.
"Here we go!"

"**Whoosh!**" laughed Gran and Grandad.